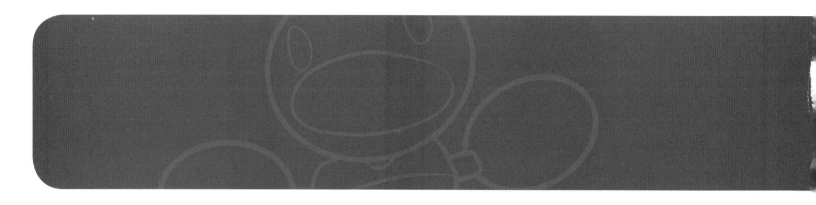

Also by Jeph Jacques:

Questionable Content Vol. 1   **Questionable Content Vol. 2**

Published by **TopatoCo Books**, a division of **The Topato Corporation.**
116 Pleasant St. Ste 203
Easthampton, MA 01027

You can read Questionable Content for free every weekday at **questionablecontent.net!**
TopatoCo is online at **topatoco.com.**

10 9 8 7 6 5 4 3 2 1
Printed in Canada

First Edition, September 2012
ISBN-13: 978-1-936561-70-4

Questionable Content Vol. 3

BY JEPH JACQUES

 TOPATOCO BOOKS *Easthampton, Massachusetts*

Introduction

Welcome to the third print collection of Questionable Content!

This is the point where the comic really started to come into its own, in my opinion. After the big Marten/Faye talk around comic 500, the focus of the strip shifted from a rather one-dimensional will-the-won't-they romance to a much broader ensemble comedy. I found myself having all sorts of ideas for new characters, story arcs, and relationships, and I suddenly had the space to explore them. While Marten and Faye remain the core of the cast, the comic isn't really "about" them anymore—it's more about the intersecting stories of a group of friends, the challenges and changes they go through, and the meandering paths they take through life.

If you're a long-time reader, thanks for sticking around. If you're new to the series, I hope you'll enjoy it. Either way, I'm glad you're here, and I look forward to meandering along with you.

— JSPH JACQCOS

Threesomes are like Communism in that you must be totally committed to the ideal or it leads to corruption and atrocities.

Can you believe vampires and zombies are EVEN MORE OF A THING, six years later?

Intravenous makeouts are over a hundred times as potent as topical makeouts.

Honestly, if you've got a urination fetish YOU should probably be the one to mention it in advance.

Large Hardon Collider hur hur hurrrr

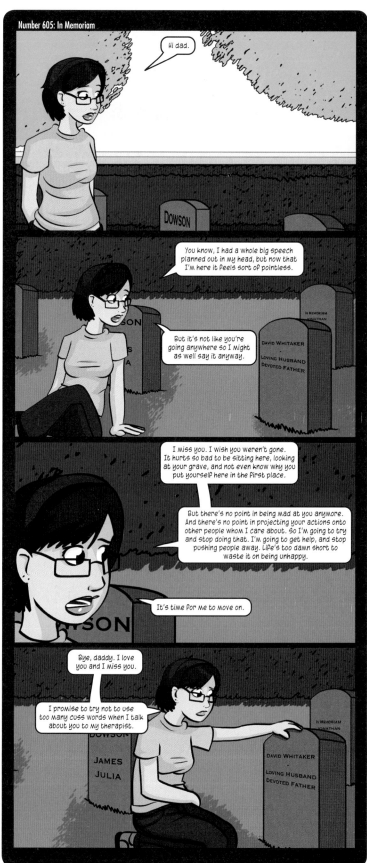

Faye probably ended up using a lot of cuss words anyway.

If she had quoted Goo Goo Dolls lyrics he would have left immediately.

Augh the waitress' head is skewed so far to the right, how did I not notice that when I drew it D:

So do you think we did the right thing?

What do you mean?

Us getting together. Do you think it was the right thing to do?

Well yeah, I mean we like each other, so...

I just feel bad for Faye. She really likes you, regardless of what her crazy-ass mind tells her. And here I am, snatching you up the minute she says she can't date you.

I dunno, it's a complicated situation. The way I see it, you gave Faye as much time as she was willing to take, you know? She TOLD me not to wait for her, and she certainly didn't say "please don't wait for me, but also don't go out with Dora."

Yeah...

Wow, this is really bothering you a lot, huh.

Part of me is the happiest girl in the world right now, but another part of me thinks I'M a horrible bitch. It's very confusing.

I think I exude a pheromone that causes existential conflict in ladies. I'm like some sort of rare Uncertainty Moth.

The wing scales of the Uncertainty Moth have a powerful hallucinogenic effect when ingested. Or maybe they don't. I'm not sure.

Hey sis. You ok?

Yeah, I'm all right. No life-changing catharsis or anything, but it was nice to visit dad.

So what do you wanna do now?

Bluh. I've had enough solemn contemplation for one day. Gimme some fast food and let's go shopping or something.

Atta girl. Medicate your grief with unhealthy food and capitalism!

Can the smartassery and get me to a Sonic post haste if you value your internal organs.

You can HAVE my uterus if you want it. It'd be nice to go a month without agonizing cramps.

Oh, excellent. "Hi Marty, I'm back from Savannah and I brought souvenirs! Here's a Confederate flag and my little sister's uterus in a jar! We can put it on the coffee table!"

From what I've seen, Marten's got enough uteruses in his life as it is.

I dunno man, that would be a pretty sweet souvenir.

10

This will become a recurring theme.

Never get blackout drunk with robots. It leads to terrible mistakes.

She kind of flails her EVERYTHING when she freaks out.

Those permits are surprisingly cheap. $40 and you can fight a lion!

...so are you worried about going back to Massachusetts?

Hmm? No, I...wow, you know, I honestly haven't worried about it at all since I got down here.

BLESS THIS HOME

Coming from you, that's a big deal. You don't think it'll be awkward or anything?

Yeah, I'm sure there'll be some uncomfortable moments. But life goes on, you know? It'll eventually work out for the best, one way or another.

How very Zen of you.

It's not Zen, it's just the way things work. Time passes, things change, and you adapt.

Aw gee Faye, all of a sudden you're like the wise, insightful big sister I never had.

It sure took me long enough. If I were Isaac Newton it would've taken a treeful of apples and a cracked skull before that whole theory of gravitation thing occurred to me.

"Isaac Newton Found Dead Under Pile Of Apples, Gravity Wanted For Questioning"

Back so soon? You really can't get enough of me.

Dora you're rad and all but right now I need to be out of my apartment as much as anything else.

What happened?

Pintsize threw a party last night while I was out, and Hannelore ended up getting smashed and possibly making out with one or more AnthroPCs. Upon realizing this, she has a panic attack.

So here I am in my filthy, disheveled apartment, trying to comfort a hyperventilating chick while Pintsize vomits cake frosting into the kitchen sink.

Poor boy! Is Hannelore okay?

Spec
• Coffee
• Scone
• Your ass

Yeah, she popped a couple Ativan and passed out on my couch. Again. Then I shut Pintsize down and disassembled him so his chassis could soak in the sink, and I managed to scrape most of the frosting and God knows what else off of the walls. So yeah, I've had a kind of crappy afternoon thus far.

So I guess now would be a bad time to tell you that I used to be a man.

No, see, the way my life works is you'd wait until after we had sex to tell me that. You know, let me get the full afterglow going before you shatter my mind.

And then Pintsize would upload video of it to the internet!

This is one of those jokes that I wouldn't make nowadays because it implies bad things about trans folks, but it never even occurred to me at the time. Sensitivities and attitudes can change a lot in six years.

The indie-rock version of the "who's on first" routine.

Oh god it looks like Amanda is staring at me in panel two and it is FREAKING ME OUT

I– I guess Steve likes superhero comics?

There is nothing more shameful than losing a fight with a sleeping man.

Caption: Marten would come to find missionary work to be extremely fulfilling.

Caption: Unicorn farts have not been proven to play a noticeable factor in climate change.

It seems like the padding could lead to chafing, though.

The horrific specter of Marten with a mustache will become a recurring theme in the comic.

17

If Marten had been hired just two weeks earlier, he would have qualified for the pegasus severance package.

Raven that is not a proper salute!

Josh was later killed in a tragic cart-racing accident. But at least he died doing what he loved.

Also the Man seriously does not give a damn about some shitty ballpoint pens.

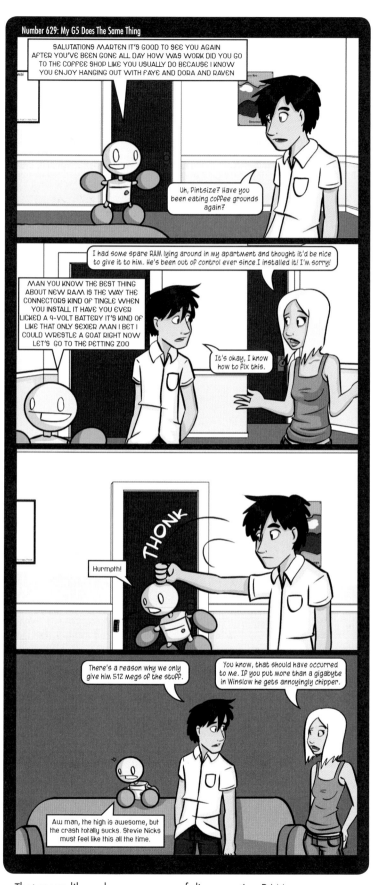

GLURK GLURK GLURK GLURK GLURK

That seems like a dangerous way of disconnecting RAM.

Later Raven would discover that the internet is full of pornography. Her mind was blown.

I'm not sure a katydid in my burrito would discourage me from eating it. Maybe I shouldn't be writing this commentary while hungry.

Hahahaha "iPods that can hold thousands of songs" ahahahaha

I got some hatemail from RealDoll owners over this strip. I dunno, they still seem really creepy to me.

Sometimes people ask me if the comics are based on real events. I am happy to say I have never had a sex dream about a piece of furniture.

I had Hanners give up smoking pretty soon. It just didn't jibe with her character.

23

I like Faye's hair in this comic, but Sven's looks like he is being attacked by some sort of gross brown octopus or sea anemone.

All that happens when you throw a sax down a flight of stairs is you make its owner very angry.

24

Shit, I should make those condoms

Hahah oh man this is one of those strips I had totally forgotten about and Marten's last line is cracking me up

Sven has some self-loathing issues.

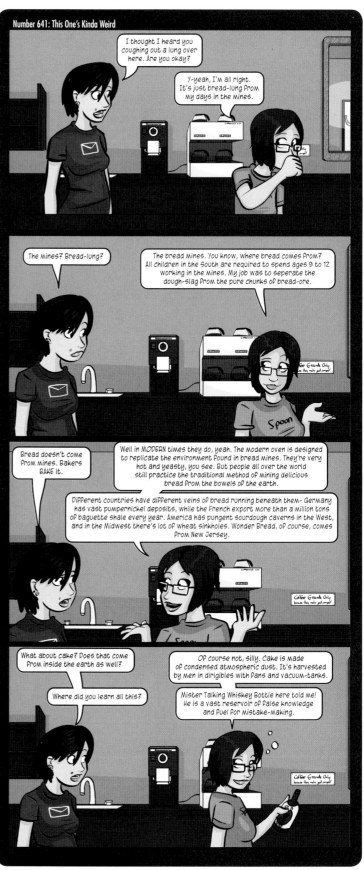

I should write a steampunk novel about bread mining.

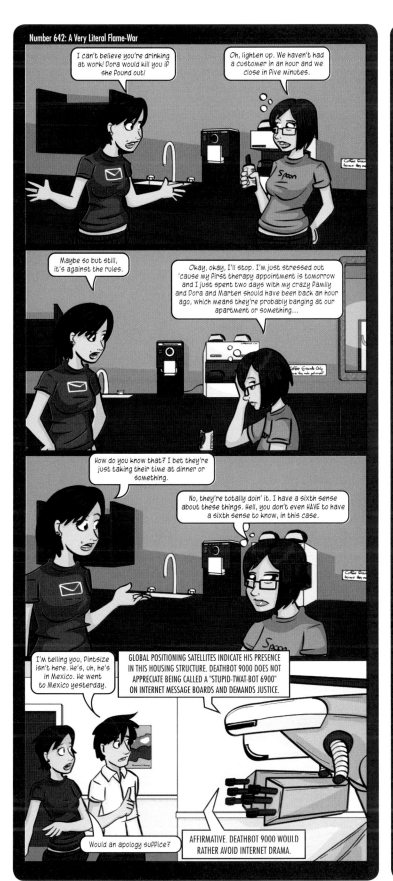

Number 642: A Very Literal Flame-War

I can't believe you're drinking at work! Dora would kill you if she found out!

Oh, lighten up. We haven't had a customer in an hour and we close in five minutes.

Maybe so but still, it's against the rules.

Okay, okay, I'll stop. I'm just stressed out 'cause my first therapy appointment is tomorrow and I just spent two days with my crazy family and Dora and Marten should have been back an hour ago, which means they're probably banging at our apartment or something...

How do you know that? I bet they're just taking their time at dinner or something.

No, they're totally doin' it. I have a sixth sense about these things. Hell, you don't even HAVE to have a sixth sense to know, in this case.

I'm telling you, Pintsize isn't here. He's, uh, he's in Mexico. He went to Mexico yesterday.

GLOBAL POSITIONING SATELLITES INDICATE HIS PRESENCE IN THIS HOUSING STRUCTURE. DEATHBOT 9000 DOES NOT APPRECIATE BEING CALLED A "STUPID-TWAT-BOT 6900" ON INTERNET MESSAGE BOARDS AND DEMANDS JUSTICE.

Would an apology suffice?

AFFIRMATIVE. DEATHBOT 9000 WOULD RATHER AVOID INTERNET DRAMA.

DEATHBOT 9000 ALSO DOES NOT APPRECIATE THE RIDICULE OF HIS OPINIONS ABOUT MY LITTLE PONY

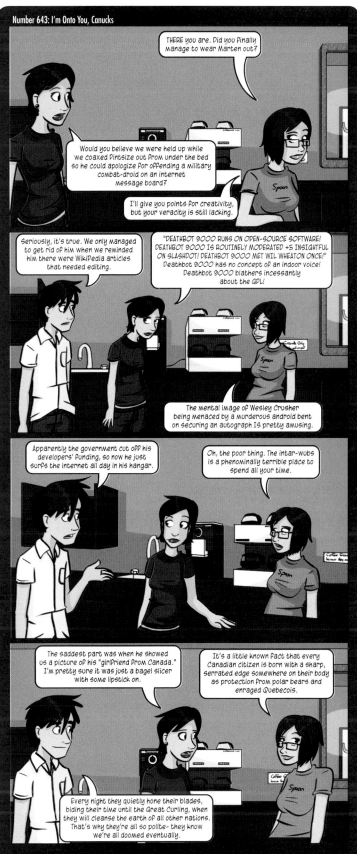

Number 643: I'm Onto You, Canucks

THERE you are. Did you finally manage to wear Marten out?

Would you believe we were held up while we coaxed Pintsize out from under the bed so he could apologize for offending a military combat-droid on an internet message board?

I'll give you points for creativity, but your veracity is still lacking.

Seriously, it's true. We only managed to get rid of him when we reminded him there were WikiPedia articles that needed editing.

"DEATHBOT 9000 RUNS ON OPEN-SOURCE SOFTWARE! DEATHBOT 9000 IS ROUTINELY MODERATED +5 INSIGHTFUL ON SLASHDOT! DEATHBOT 9000 MET WIL WHEATON ONCE!" Deathbot 9000 has no concept of an indoor voice! Deathbot 9000 blathers incessantly about the GPL!

The mental image of Wesley Crusher being menaced by a murderous android bent on securing an autograph IS pretty amusing.

Apparently the government cut off his developers' funding, so now he just surfs the internet all day in his hangar.

Oh, the poor thing. The intar-wubs is a phenomenally terrible place to spend all your time.

The saddest part was when he showed us a picture of his "girlfriend from Canada." I'm pretty sure it was just a bagel slicer with some lipstick on.

It's a little known fact that every Canadian citizen is born with a sharp, serrated edge somewhere on their body as protection from polar bears and enraged Quebecois.

Every night they quietly hone their blades, biding their time until the Great Curling, when they will cleanse the earth of all other nations. That's why they're all so polite- they know we're all doomed eventually.

Still pretty sure this is true about Canadians

One Van To Bring Them All, And In The Darkness Drive Them To 7–11

It seems like arm-wrestling a Pope would be pretty easy, they tend to be old and somewhat frail

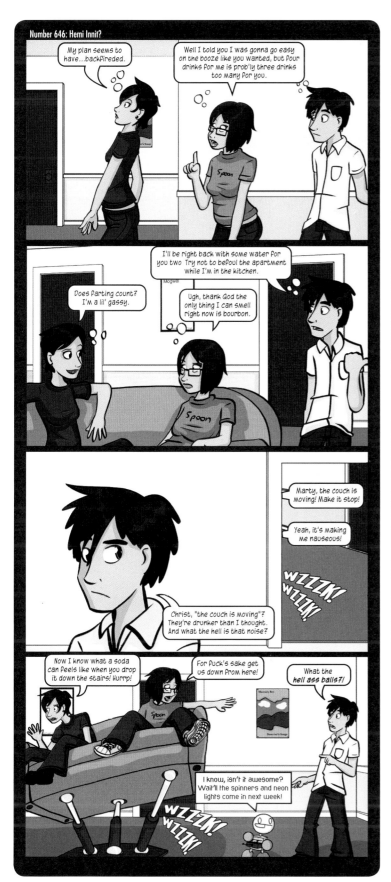

Oh my god look at Marten's bellbottoms

Those condoms have been in that couch for like 10 years

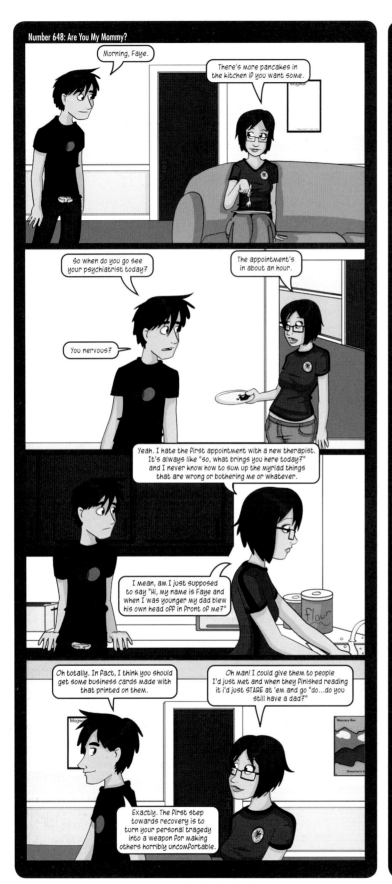

Gettin' a pretty strong Randy Millholland vibe from this strip. Mean and twisted >:)

Pretty sure if you've had a lobotomy it doesn't really matter how well you can see.

My first attempt at a crowd scene! Crowd scenes take FOREVER to draw.

Last I heard our local alternative newspaper was basically being run out of a closet at the local mainstream newspaper. I'm glad I got out when I did.

This is another one of those strips that I think has held up really well over time.

Can you half-ass indifference?

"Heck-butt" is the more socially acceptable version of "hell-ass."

Faye's smile in panel 4 is positively PREDATORY.

I once worked out the coffee shop's schedule based on how many employees they had and at this point Dora would've been working 100 hour weeks D:

Franz Ferdinand's hit song "Take Me Out" was a direct reference to the assassination of the historical Franz Ferdinand.

I've got Smooshed Titties' first EP, it's pretty good

Stomped: A Grindcore Musical

35

Keytars: slightly less embarassing than a Chapman Stick

"Toss me," Boromir said to Aragorn. "Just don't tell the elf."

From this point on, Hannelore's hair basically got poofier and poofier.

I eventually wrote and recorded an ENTIRE ACTUAL ALBUM of metal songs about a unicorn prince.

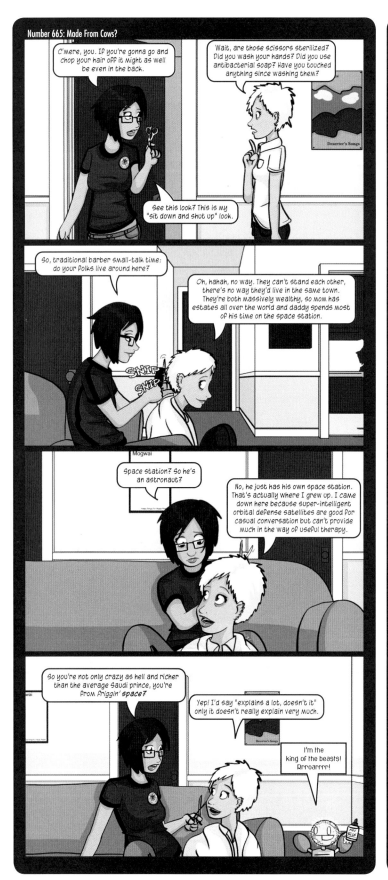

I wonder if we will ever get to see that space station. HMMMMM

Seriously, I had this strip all planned out since like comic 200.

No idea what I was doing with the speech bubble order in panel 3 there, sorry.

This is the first strip to reference the social status and rights of AI in the QC universe. I've tried to handle it with a light touch (as I'm not sure how well it would actually hold up under scrutiny).

Wait, if you've got such bad OCD, how come you smoke and have like ten ear piercings?

A girl has to have SOME glaring contradictions in her life.

I have never seen a chick down a double of JIM Beam that quickly before.

The first one goes down quickly so the others can take their time.

Whew, okay. No crazy chicks in sight and I'm sober enough to tell the difference between a urinal and a sink. I'm in the clear.

Marten! You gotta help me!

Gah! NEVER startle a man when he's doin' his bathroom thing! Sudden urethral shutoff is extremely unpleasant and may lead to spattering!

One of my psychotic exes has been following me around all day. You have to distract her so I can escape!

What's in it for me?

The eternal gratitude and approbation of your girlfriend's older brother?

Got any nickels instead? Those are more useful.

Sven you are such a douche

40

Such a douuuuuuuche

41

"She's literally trying to cut my throat!" "Yep, that's normal for Faye."

Marten's line in panel 4 found its way onto a bunch of "famous quotes" websites and gets retweeted by hundreds of people to this day. It's weird.

Sven and Genevieve have a very healthy relationship

Sven and Faye are about to have a very healthy relationship

I think it was at this point that "Faye threatens violence" had worn out its welcome as a punchline. PUNCHline! GET IT?! HAHAHAohgodI'msorry

Faye that is werewolves you are thinking of, and that is a very insensitive word to use.

And a "C" for "comeuppance."

Last call is always five minutes too early.

Pretty sure the last thing you feel like doing after getting a course of rabies shots is to have sex.

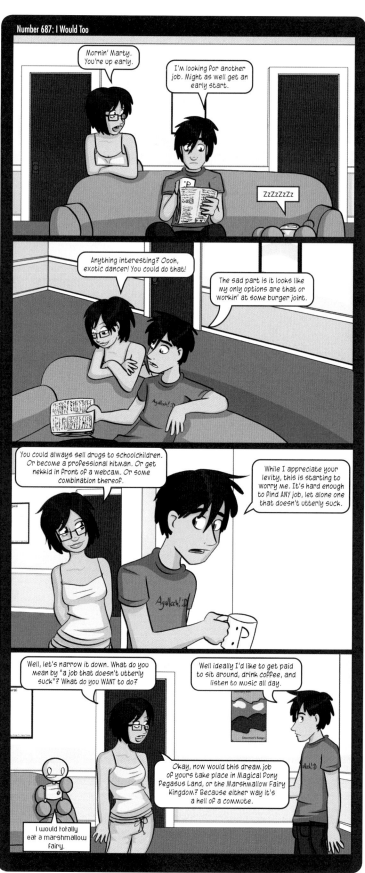

Marten pretty much described my job, only without the crushing self-doubt and awful sleep schedule.

Seriously, Ayn Rand was a terrible writer with terrible opinions

Damn, I really wanna try a cayenne mocha now, actually.

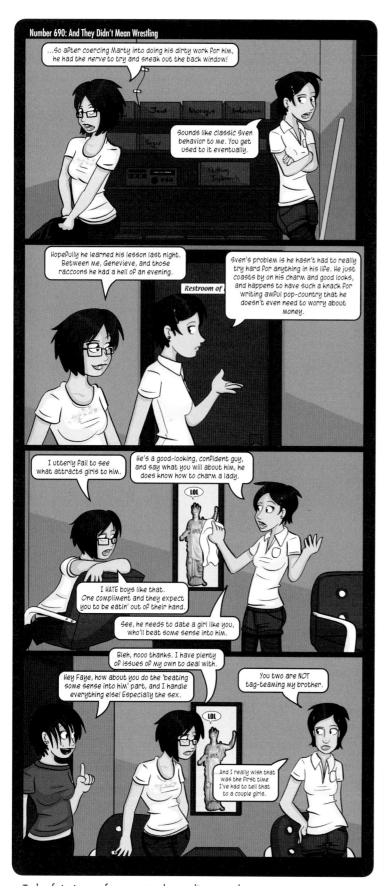

To be fair, it was for an actual wrestling match.

Librarians love webcomics.

Hey sweetie, what's up?

I got a job!

Omigod, really?

Well, I PROBABLY got a job. It's not official yet, but the front desk person at the Smif library said I should just show up tomorrow morning for training anyway.

That's awesome!

Working in the library at an all-girls college? Why not have him wax the pews at a convent or bartend at a brothel while you're at it?

I imagine bartending at a convent would be more fun than either. Nuns know how to party. Nuns roll deep.

I'd totally just get the older nuns drunk and listen to them tell stories about the Nun Wars.

Nun Wars?

Back in 1947, all the nuns from around the world got together to determine which order was most bad-ass among God's servants.

Every five years they commemorate the great battle with a reenactment.

Hah, holy LARPing! "My other oversized foam weapon is THE LORD."

If I ever start up my own pub I will name it the Drunken Nun.

...So the Poor Clares were surrounded by the Sisters of Mercy, when artillery support finally arrived.

Artillery support?

Bibles fired from trebuchets.

I hate to interrupt, but I'm taking Marten out to lunch to celebrate his new employment.

Sure, if by "lunch" you mean "hot sex" and by "celebrate" you also mean "hot sex".

Actually right now I'd rather have a "hot cheeseburger", thanks.

I don't even want to KNOW what that's a euphemism for.

Hmph. All "ooh look at us we're such a happy couple. Watch as we go off to lunch holding hands and giggling! La la la blargh argiblagh blech."

Aww, are you jealous?

Absolutely not! Just because I haven't so much as made out with a boy in years doesn't mean I'm jealous.

And the vibrant shade of green isn't envy. I just...ate a lot of chlorophyll this morning.

Eww, you eat salad for breakfast? No wonder you're cranky. And gassy.

Dammit I told you that smell earlier was NOT ME!

FART JOEKS

You can tell I was really tired by the time I finished panel 4 because of how skewed their heads are.

Wait, since when does Pintsize have blood?

Northampton is a weird town.

Damn, Marten!

Dora that is not a very ladylike pose

Being the straight man (or lady) at Coffee of Doom is a thankless task.

Faye treats personal boundaries like neutrinos treat conventional matter. OH YEAH SCIENCE HUMOR ALL UP IN HERE

That's really more of a Cinemax thing.

Faye why are you straddling the counter in panel 2 that is just weird

Raven has switched from using lube to straight-up shellac.

Good thing she didn't spring for the deluxe model, it comes equipped with a Glock 19.

Silly Winslow, your job is to provide comic relief.

Winslow, you have PLENTY of purpose! You keep me company, you can do all kinds of computery things like run programs and play music...

Oh! Okay, I feel much better now.

Heh, you AnthroPCs have it easy. Us humans have been tryin' to figure out our purpose for thousands of years now.

As far as I can tell, your chief genetic imperatives are mating and killing each other.

It's all genetics. We wanna mate so we can raise children, and we fight because we want our children to have the most resources.

Heh, yeah pretty much.

And it's self-selecting, too. People who choose not to listen to those primordial instincts necessarily remove themselves from the gene pool.

I don't think it's that simple. Individuals who don't reproduce themselves can still affect to the gene pool by helping raise others' offspring.

See, you're still just trying to ensure the survival of the species. Heck, what's the most intimate thing humans do together? Mate! Even if you're not trying to reproduce, you're still doing what your genes want you to do.

So you're basically saying that we're all just automatons following programs encoded in our genes?

No, you make everything WAY too complicated for it to be pure instinct. Dating? Flowers? MYSPACE? I mean, come on.

Haha! "Interests: Sports, video games, fulfilling genetic imperatives by stickin' my wee-wee in some vaginas."

oh man remember Myspace

...Actually, the worst part about growing up on a space station was the music.

The music?

The sight of the sun rising over the curve of the earth is majestic and all, but you get REALLY sick of having to listen to "Thus Spake Zarathustra" every time.

BAM!

All right bitches, where's that pansy-ass vacuum?! Because I am going to go Miyamoto Musashi on its ass! Assuming it has one.

Where the hell did you get THAT?

Home shopping channel.

So you've had this for a while then? Just in case some situation arose where you would need full samurai regalia?

Well yeah. What's your point?

Is there a word for when somebody does something completely illogical, but in a perfectly logical manner? Because I really could use that word right now.

I don't like the way this arms race is escalating. Pretty soon they'll be charging each other with those ridiculously huge swords from Final Fantasy 7.

My Limit Break involves a moose, the demon Baphomet, and a Kuiper Belt object. It takes four hours and you can't skip any of the cutscenes.

Man remember when Final Fantasy games were actually good

This strip would be a lot funnier if I had removed those last two bits of dialog. I feel like I've gotten a lot better at paring jokes down since then.

Okay, totally lollin' at Pintsize's last line. Sometimes extending a punchline can lead to great things.

I wonder if we'll be seeing more of this guy in the future.

Dora is somewhat unclear on what veganism is, apparently.

So do you like my hair?

It looks good, but it makes you taller than me.

I still say it makes you look like a goth cassowary.

If I'm a cassowary then I'm the...hey, is that Steve over there?

It is! And he's with a girl!

And that girl is not Ellen! I smell mischief. Let's go investigate, Marty.

Hey, Steve! What's up man?

Oh uh hey Marten, not too much.

Who's your lady-friend? Does Ellen know about this dangerous liason?

No, she doesn't. We, uh, broke up. Again.

No, see, this is the part where you're supposed to be all "oh I was just giving this young lady directions to the nearest church so she could go pray" and we all laugh because HAHA WHAT A WACKY MISUNDERSTANDING.

Wait a minute, who's Ellen?

I think the sheer level of awkwardness has rendered me sterile.

Don't worry Marten, all the drunken headbutts to your crotch had already taken care of that.

Dude, what happened with you and Ellen this time?

She accepted a position on a deep-sea research vessel for next semester. She thought it would be best if we just ended things now before we got too serious.

Oh man, that's rough. She didn't even want to try the long-distance ship-to-shore thing?

Well, I...took it badly. There was some arguing, some heated words were said. Some things about our respective sexual abilities that I think neither of us really meant, but...

Oooh, ouch.

Well, maybe if you give her a day or two to cool off you can patch things back together...

I don't think there's much left to patch, unfortunately.

What do you mean?

Well, when she slammed the door in my face I probably shouldn't have shouted "I hope you contract dolphin-syphilis" at the top of my lungs.

Hmm, yeah. That was probably a mistake.

As long as she packs some condoms she should be safe. Better make them Magnums, male dolphins are pretty hung.

My wife had a friend who trained dolphins to find underwater mines for the Navy SEALs. He apparently hated working with female dolphins because they would constantly proposition him.

Back in the day I would stay up late and watch the knife show on home shopping network for the sheer comedy value.

Are YOU that dude?

That's not homoerotic, that's homoromantic!

The nearest real-world equivalent is George T. Stagg Family Reserve. If you've got a couple hundred dollars to spend on a bottle of booze, you'll find nothing finer.

I still think that's a really good slogan for a bottle of liquor. If you own a distillery, shoot me an email and we'll talk licensing.

The Beast Of Bourbon can poop with the lid down because he is incorporeal.

What the hell?

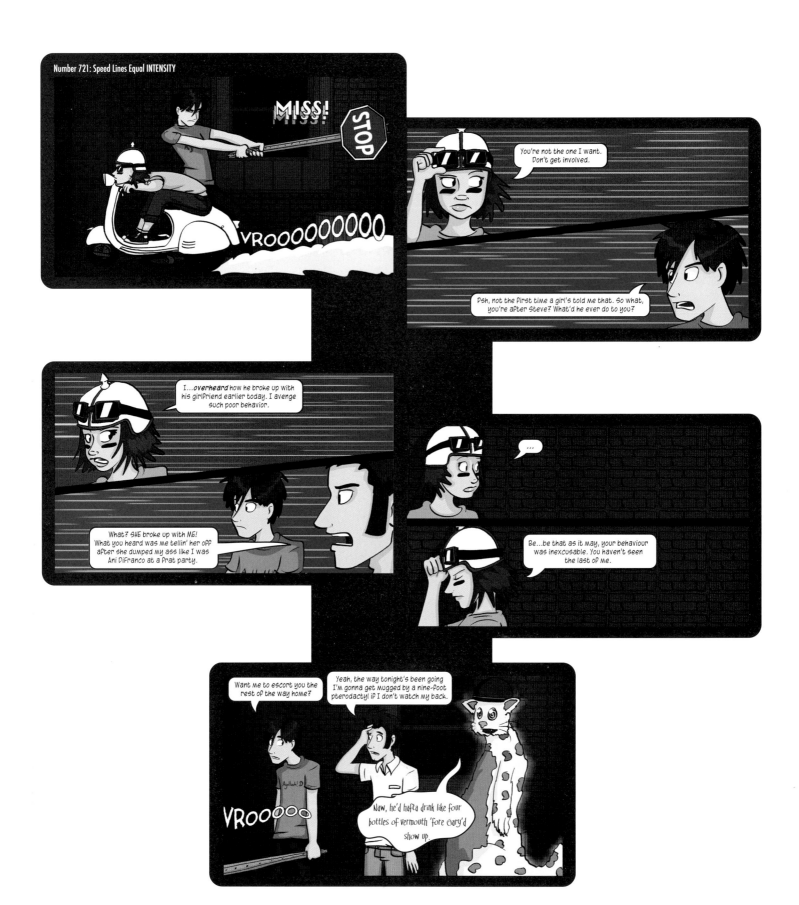

ANIME

Dora would still think it was hot.

Hannelore likes to pretend that the last Indiana Jones movie never happened.

What kind of noise does a springbok make?

PENELOPE YOU STOLE MY HAT, GIVE IT BACK

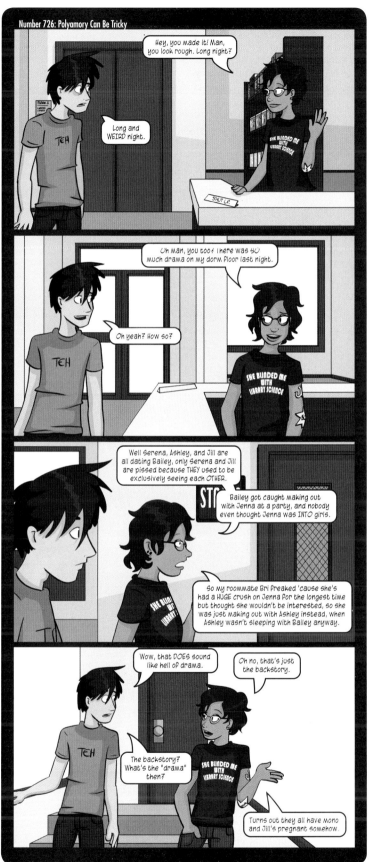

Ah, college romance.

AH, COLLEGE ROMANCE

My liberal arts degrees is directly responsible for my career as a cartoonist (in that it ensured I would be almost entirely unemployable)

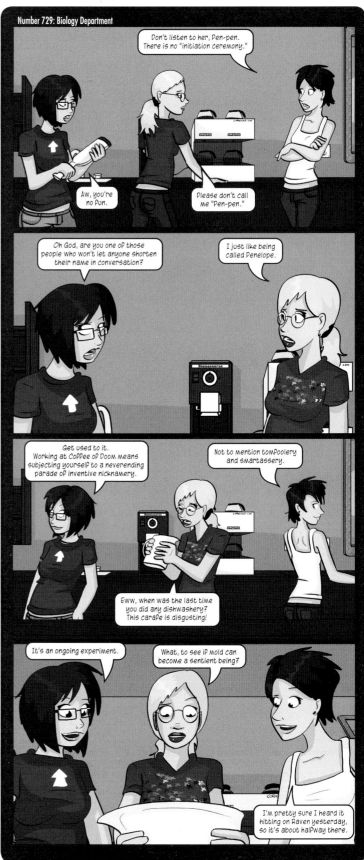

Dora keeps changing hairstyles to this day. I've just never been able to settle on one for her. It's weird.

Pintsize is widely regarded as the foremost toenail connoisseur on the East Coast.

The strip clubs in Western MA are all really depressing. That is, even more depressing than your average strip club.

That is the second most illegal business model I have ever come up with. I'm not allowed to talk about the first.

So what Faye is saying is that her prank ended up being way more trouble than it was worth.

Hur hur "ball" hur hur

Coffee of Doom is very progressive about their oppression.

Damn, Marten!

Damn, Marten.

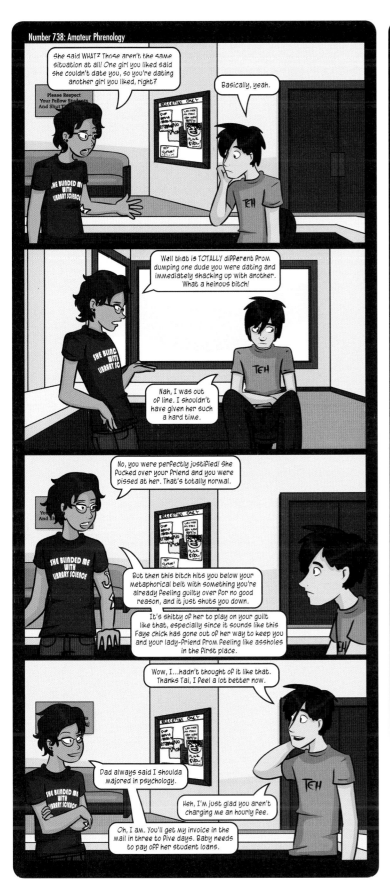

There was so much arguing on my forums about these last couple comics. Apparently people on the internet have a hard time with the concept that both parties can be in the wrong in an argument.

I wonder if there are any plaid AnthroPC chassis

It's...it's not actually that sexy you guys :(

When you think about it, The Hulk is just one big green boner metaphor.

Death Cab is even MORE expensive to hire these days.

This story was an experiment. I wanted to try something a little weirder, to show how different the QC universe is from our own.

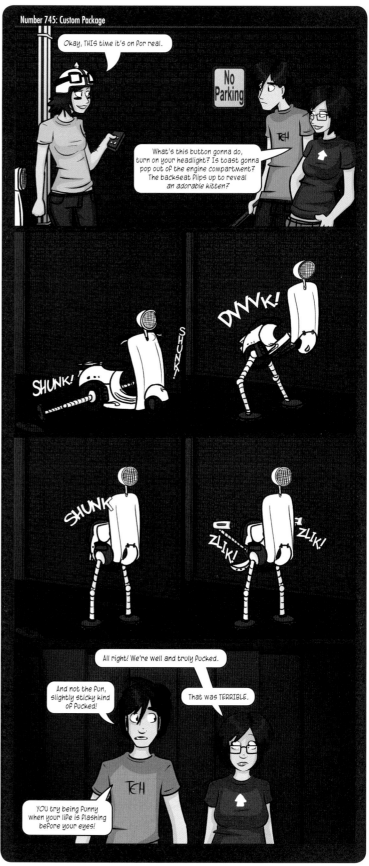

Looking back on it now, it doesn't really fit the tone of the rest of the comic, but I still think it's got some good moments.

That robot scooter design is...not one of the good moments. :\

HA / HA / HA / HA

Pretty much the entire story was a lead-up to that punchline, which I STILL think totally rules.

Yes Marten, exactly.

Northampton cops are pretty chill

POLITICAL HUMOR

Do Not Feed The Baristas (They Bite)

Dad Rocker is weirdly self-aware.

I really wanted to make that shirt but couldn't do the full-size screen printing it would have required.

Elephant seals are pretty cranky.

Penelope is given to ranting.

Verbal tennis is much less strenuous than the real thing.

This cannot end well.

Yup, called it.

It's in her bellybutton

Chinese Delivery Man, Pizza Girl's arch-nemesis!

W-where has she been kissing Sven?

The stuffed bunny would later find religion and become completely insufferable.

Think how much more work we would get done if our genitalia had opposable thumbs.

Mornin' Tai.

Hey Marten.

SHUT UP.

So Bailey and I had "the talk" last night.

Ooh. How'd that go?

Well I finally broke down and confessed my feelings for her, and she said she thought I was a total sweetheart but she just didn't feel the same way about me.

Ooh, ouch. I know how that goes.

Yeah...then I ended up getting drunk with Serena and Ashley, and one thing led to another and we, uh, kind of all hooked up.

I didn't either, before last night.

Wow okay, nevermind. I don't know how that goes.

So you're happy with how it worked out, then?

Oh heck yeah! Threesomes are awesome. You should try it sometime!

No thanks. I went through enough trouble to land ONE girl. A bird in the hand's worth two in the bush, you know?

After last night, I feel like an ornithologist.

Tai's favorite bird is the Greater Pied Pussywarbler.

Whatcha readin'?

Oh, just some godawful romance novel. "Drusilla of Borehelm Manor," by Rutherford Wainwright Ashecrofte.

I wouldn't have figured you for the romance-novel type.

I know, right? But I can't stop reading! It's so florid and overwrought, like a Meatloaf album in printed form.

I mean, check out this passage: "Drusilla's ample bosoms, engorged with ill-concealed lust for the dashing young Lord Forwhyllyn, strained against her bustier like half-wild horses straining against their new master's bridle."

Huh. I think I know the guy who wrote that. It sounds really familiar.

Really? What's he like? Does he live in a castle and write all of his novels by candle-light with a crowquill pen? Frilly shirt half-unbuttoned, Fabio hair blowing in the chill evening breeze as he refills his snifter of congnac?

More like a trailer, a manuscript consisting of bar napkins and toilet paper, filthy flannel shirt with missing buttons, passed out in a pool of Milwaukee's Best with the air conditioner dripping onto his dingy trucker hat.

Oh man, that's even better. I should book him as a guest lecturer for my creative writing class.

That's a great idea. You know, I'm also friends with Kim Jong Il and I bet he'd LOVE to come lead an ethics roundtable.

Jimbo writes a mean romance novel.

Hey, where's the cranky brunette today?

Who, Faye? Sleeping in, probably. She's got the morning off.

Oh. Well crap, who am I supposed to get my daily dose of contrariness from then?

Don't look at me, I'm busy looking up diseases. Try Penelope over there.

The new girl? I dunno...

Um, hey. Can I get a cup of coffee?

Sure. What size?

Small?

I, uh, no thanks.

Cream and sugar?

Augh, this isn't working! You're not even Methadone to Faye's heroin. I gotta get my fix or the shakes will start!

How about we use that other tried-and-true Faye maneuver and I bop you on the head with a carafe?

Hmm. WebMD doesn't say anything about concussions being used to treat addiction.

If you hit a drug addict on the head they will probably just want more drugs to dull the pain :(

So you really know the guy who wrote "Drusilla?"

I think so. I drink at the same bar as him, if I'm not mistaken.

Please Respect Your Fellow Students And Shut The Hell Up!

Really? Do you think he'd be there tonight?

He's as much of a fixture there as the bar's actual fixtures.

Would you mind introducing me to him?

I guess not, but I don't quite get your fascination.

His book is trashy, poorly-written, incredibly sexist towards BOTH genders, and the most entertaining thing I've read all year. Why WOULDN'T I want to meet him?

I dunno, it can be disappointing to realize your idols aren't all they're cracked up to be.

From what you've told me, I'm expecting a slovenly redneck whose eyes will glaze over with disinterest the moment he sees I don't have much in the way of cleavage.

Lack of cleavage might not faze him, depending on how drunk he is. One night I saw him hitting on the pinball machine.

Oh, so he's more of a junk-in-the-trunk kind of guy? I don't have much goin' on down there either.

Actually, I've been drawing Tai with quite the booty lately. So I guess she just has low butt-self-esteem.

I wonder if there is a place that will do bespoke Pope hats.

MY TUMESCENCE ACHES FOR YOUR ATTENTIONS STOP

I dunno, the Old Testament is pretty good if you're into that sort of thing. Yahweh was kind of a jerk!

The couple that jokes about necrophilia together...uh...probably isn't welcome at funerals?

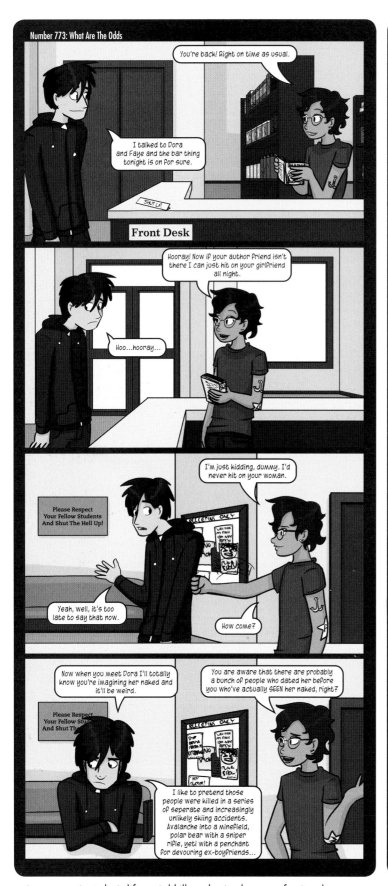

Angry, sentient chair lift, serial killer who is also a professional snowboarder...

Once again, Penelope goes off on a rant.

Give a hobo booze and he'll drink for a day. Teach him to distill his own booze and he'll probably end up in prison for moonshining.

I had ear surgery back in high school and had to wear this bizarre earmuff bandage thing for weeks. It was way more embarrassing than a cone would've been.

We can't stop here, this is moose country!

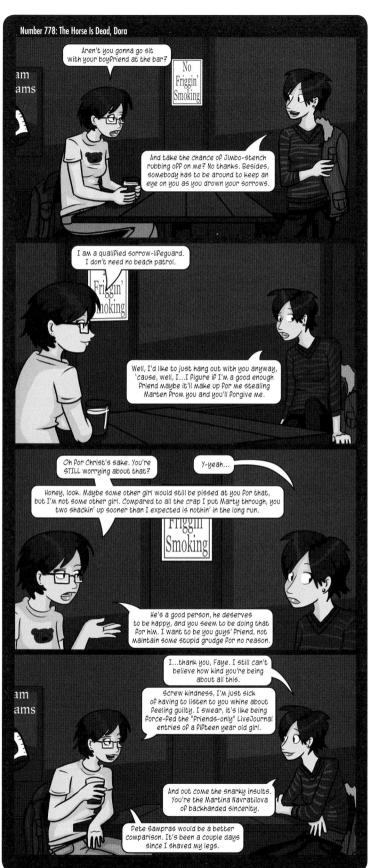

Man, those are some dated tennis references.

It hasn't happened yet!

I feel like you'd have to throw someone pretty hard to put them through a plate-glass window. Those things are thick!

I shoulda motion-blurred him more, I think.

That is a preposterous name. I LOVE IT.

Q: If you kiss a jackass, what does it turn into? A: A somewhat confused jackass.

Ceci N'est Pas Une Prank

This is strip still makes me laugh and I DON'T KNOW WHY

SPEAKING of perspective, what's up with that bookshelf behind Marten! Heyooo!

I seriously used my bachelor's degree as a coaster for a while

It's like a death pool, only sexier.

I'm impressed that Marten was able to get out all that dialogue in panel 4 in one breath.

The French teacher at my high school was fond of mixing aphorisms like this.

TURKEYS Raven's dreams are crumbling before her :(

They would probably have to go to the hospital and thus would not be able to enjoy the scotch.

Faye those burns are so sick the CDC would like to have a word with you

Twenty minutes to enjoy it, four hours of regret later.

Number 797: Break Out The Polygraph

Create Your Own Burrito
Rice, Beans, Greens, Cheese and Sauce

DRINK

Bus Your Goddamn Table Hippie

As much as I appreciate you buying me lunch, I have to ask what you're trying to accomplish with all this.

What do you mean?

I mean all this "turning over a new leaf" and "trying to avoid sketchy ex-sex" stuff. It's not like you.

I dunno...when you confronted me outside the bar that one night, it made me feel like an asshole. I thought maybe I should try to be less of one.

I could just punch you every time you do something stupid. You'll either suffer brain damage or become a better person. Or both.

Heh, it may in fact come to that. I'm really bad at doing anything that doesn't come easily to me. Being a non-asshole may be one of those things.

Now, was that unexpected honesty, or a cynical attempt to get me to feel sorry for you?

I...uh...dammit, I've been charming girls for so long now I even can't tell when I'm being sincere.

So is THAT honesty, or are you still just trying for the pity-points?

Probably both at once. I'm a Quantum Jerk.

As Einstein put it, "God does not play dice with the universe. Only a jerk would do that."

Number 798: Picky Picky

So what's the deal with you "only dating blondes"?

It's not that I won't DATE girls who aren't blond, it's just that I PREFER blondes. And I can afford to be pretty picky about who I sleep with, so it mostly ends up being blond chicks.

What a delightfully arbitrary, egotistic standard to hold others to.

How is it any more arbitrary than your standards? You tend to be attracted to skinny indie-rock dudes, right?

Your point being?

It's not that you won't DATE dudes who don't fit that template, but that's the portion of the population you're initially most attracted to.

And yeah, it might be egotistic for me to say that I can get girls pretty easily, but it's also mostly true in my experience. So why wouldn't I apply my standards to those girls I try and get?

So what's the rest of your standard-set look like? "Blond, dumb, hot, and willing to put out on the first date?"

Hey, I've dated plenty of smart girls!

Okay, replace "dumb" with "gullible".

I...uh...okay, I'll give you that one. Why is it the more I talk to you the more I feel like a misogynist prick?

It's my mutant superpower. I was bitten by a radioactive Ani DiFranco.

Ooh, that's another one of my rules. No Ani DiFranco fans.

That is a difficult rule to abide by in Northampton.

101

If Raven is a Highlander, we are all doomed.

I took a Trazodone to help me sleep once and I was pretty much this out of it the next day.

Anxiety about anxiety, another comic torn straight from the pages of my life.

Tai's browser history is 99% pictures of kittens, she's just self-conscious about it.

If you gaze too long into the porn, the porn gazes back into you.

Man, killer whales are JERKS.

Winslow's expressions are all just animated gifs.

It's actually Jack Daniel, Dora. Fun fact: he died of a toe infection.

Hangovers, no matter how awful, are rarely enough to put one off booze forever.

I JACK OFF A LOT IS WHAT I AM TRYING TO SAY

Number 809: Devil's Advocate

"No, I don't think we need to schedule another appointment" is another one.

Number 810: And Now You Will Too

To this day, no one has ever topped "Happy Birthday, Grandma!"

IT SURE WOULD BE MORE INTERESTING THAN THIS CURRENT STORY HA HAHA HA HLGBUALGHLGHL #selfburns

Sorry Penny but I don't think you're protagonist material.

Plans within plans, pizzas within pizzas.

Snaphiroth is my OTP

The shark is all confused because what the hell is a bear doing in the middle of the great barrier reef?

Aw, she sounds sweet!

They shut that home down but none of the tenants noticed :(

Seems like a pretty mellow psychotic break to me.

Number 819: Homage To Kill Bill

Let's see...bread, beer, chips, cheese, chicken, salad mix, more beer, hamburger, hamburger helper, pasta...

EVERYTHING 50% Marked Up!

Bu- aw, dammit! That Penelope chick was totally HOT and TALKING TO ME and here I am going GROCERY SHOPPING? What the hell is wrong with me? What happened to the Steve-mojo?

I should go back there, but... What's the point? I missed my chance, I'd probably just screw it up now anyway. Christ, I really WOULD be better off meeting chicks at the morgue.

I could arrange that.

Excuse me?

I said I could arrange that. I work at the county morgue.

Do you usually go around offering this service to random dudes on the street?

No, but it's not every day I run into a guy muttering to himself out loud about wanting to meet dead ladies.

No no, I don't wanna meet DEAD chicks, I-

Ohhh, you like 'em warm but not all struggly? I have a friend who works in the ICU at the hospital, he could probably hook you up.

Don't do it Steve, remember what happened in Kill Bill!

Number 820: She's Not Really Helping

Seriously though, what's got you all bummed out and muttering about bangin' dead chicks?

I don't wanna bang dead chicks, I...no, you know what, I'm not gonna bother you with my bullshit. You don't even know me.

Aw c'mon, now I'm all curious. You're being so pathetic and whiny there's GOTTA be a good reason behind it.

That's the thing, there isn't one. A girl I liked broke up with me, and now it has me all doubting my ability with the ladies and what I'm looking for in the first place. I'm just being stupid.

Maybe you're gay.

I'm not GAY, I'm just undergoing a period of self-examination.

I'll BET you are. With your HAND.

Actually, not really.

Really? Not once since you last got it on?

Nope. Haven't felt like it.

I'd make a sarcastic remark, but I just realized I'm talking to a stranger about his masturbation habits.

It's oddly liberating, actually. This must be what confession feels like to a Catholic.

Forgive me, father, for I have jacked off a whole bunch of times

112

So you really work at the morgue?

Yep! I'm a pathologist's assistant.

How'd you end up with that gig?

I passed the secret initiation rite in med school. If you can spend five minutes with your head in the body cavity of a fresh cadaver without freaking out or throwing up, you qualify.

It wasn't that hard. They give you a snorkel.

And all the gore and weird smells don't bother you?

You'd be amazed what you can get used to. The only thing that still bothers me is the brains. Decomposing brains look almost exactly like cake batter. I haven't been able to bake since I took the job.

Wow, suddenly Pintsize's love of cake mix seems a lot more sinister.

Pintsize, eh. Pet of yours?

Nah, he's my friend's AnthroPC.

Oh man, those things are more trouble than they're worth. We had to settle a nasty lawsuit when our recordkeeping AnthroPC used a severed head as a marionette to "cheer up" some cancer patients.

It was really more like HALF a severed head.

...So then he's all "I just love EXOTIC women like you." I'm like "Exotic? What exactly do you mean by that? I'm not some mysterious courtesan from a foreign land, asshole, I'm third-generation American! So it's my skin color? I've got more melanin than you and that makes me more INTERESTING somehow?

Yeah, "exotic" is a word I associate more with "tropical diseases" than "appealing qualities in a woman."

Haha! Yeah, that date was about as fun as a good case of ebola.

You know what they say- it isn't a good date unless you're bleeding from every orifice, including your pores, by the end of the night.

Trash

I keep a belt sander in my bedroom for just that purpose.

See, it's not the color of her skin, it's how much flesh she is willing to flay off your bones that determines a chick's exotitude.

Wait hang on, are we flirting now?

I'm not sure. I'm intrigued yet kind of freaked out at the same time. God, this must be how Marten feels all the time. Poor bastard.

Looking back, I really like morgue girl's character design.

113

If you don't know who the jerk is in your circle of friends, it's probably you!

The most passive-aggressive serial killer of all time.

"He had big, bushy sideburns." "Hey, so do I! What a coincidence!"

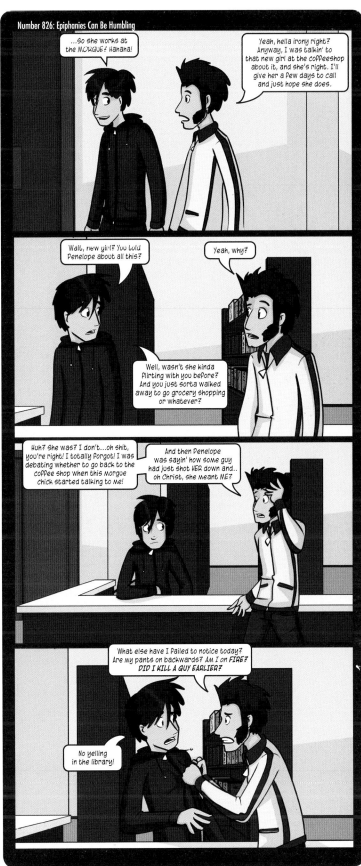

A+ punchline in this one, good job me

You have the right to remain silent, but it'll be kind of awkward if you do.

Hey, a callback joke!

You know they'd just end up giving each other giant fake hickies with the suction cups.

If you get aroused by the sight of Sean Connery in a bright red diaper, there is probably something wrong with you.

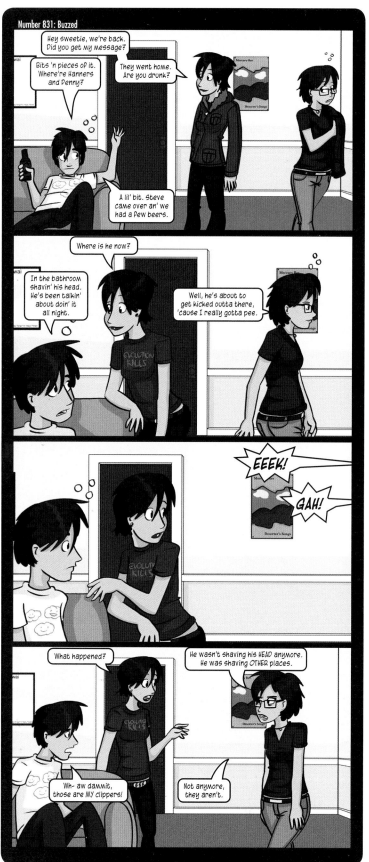

His...his chest, right?

Viva la revolucion

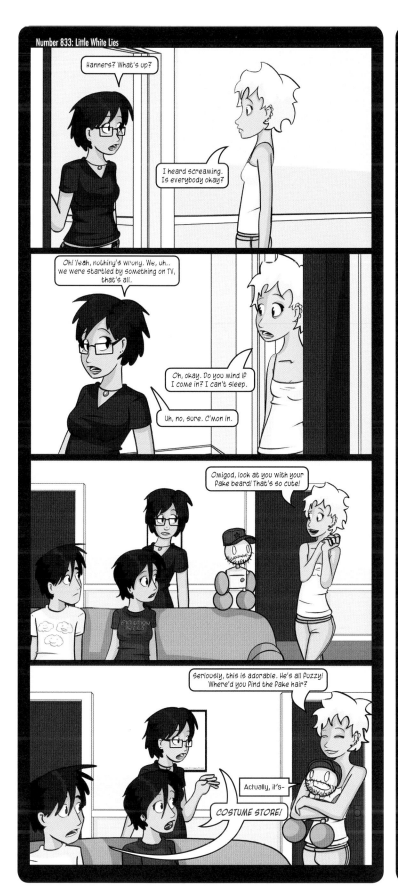

Hanners? What's up?

I heard screaming. Is everybody okay?

Oh! Yeah, nothing's wrong. We, uh.. we were startled by something on TV, that's all.

Oh, okay. Do you mind if I come in? I can't sleep.

Uh, no, sure. C'mon in.

Omigod, look at you with your fake beard! That's so cute!

Seriously, this is adorable. He's all fuzzy! Where'd you find the fake hair?

Actually, it's—

COSTUME STORE!

To this day, she has no idea.

Hey kiddo, you missed some serious hijinks last night after you went home.

Oh?

Steve got drunk, cut off most of his hair, and buzzed his sack.

And how do you know that last delightful tidbit of information?

It's, uh...it's a long story. You really had to be there.

But it's probably good that you weren't.

So did he spend the whole evening pining over his mysterious random-encounter chick?

Not really.

Did he say anything about me?

Not really.

So you won't tell me what the "hijinks" were and Steve didn't say anything interesting about me or that girl he likes. What's the point of this conversation?

Now next time you see Steve, your first thought will be "his junk is totally bald right now."

It'll defuse any awkwardness! Or make it worse. We get entertainment either way.

Right now you are thinking about a cartoon character's shaved scrotum. YOU'RE WELCOME

The girls' attempt to unionize would be brutally thwarted by riot police.

Nat is basically every bad doom metal band ever.

Raven is a trusting soul.

At least she remembered to wear some.

pffffhahahah oh my god dora's face in panel 4 ahahahaha

The earth is splitting in twain! The Beast is rising from the depths! Goddamnit, you've ushered in the end of days!

Scientists initially mistook Dora's afterglow for a new supernova.

Wait, what was the entire board of trustees doing in the library at 4am on a Saturday morning?

That seems like the sort of thing you'd probably want to get out in the open on the first date.

Maybe TWO tour buses!

Amir's book "How To Make Out Like A Pro" would later spend six weeks on the New York Times bestseller list.

What do you think robots DO when people leave the factory at the end of the day?

I have a feeling Cage would approve.

MAYBE SHE DIDN'T :O #ghosts #spookyghosts

Yippie kai yay

Sobbing and laughing the whole time.

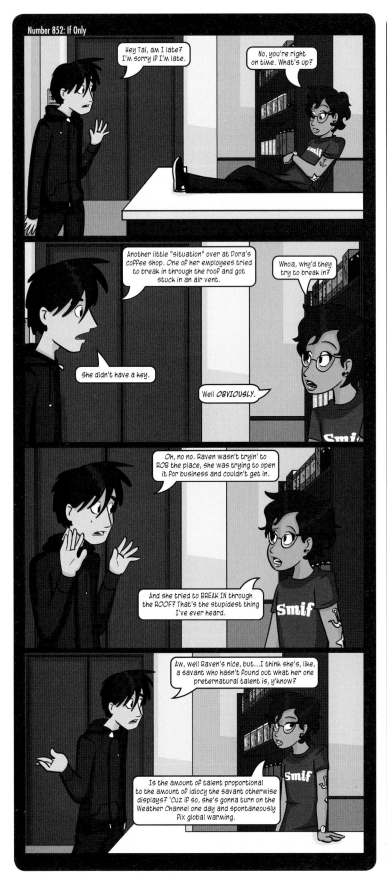

Unfortunately, Raven only watches sitcoms.

Insanity is doing the same action over and over and expecting a different outcome.

128

You're awfully mean to that Angus guy.

He deserves it.

IF you REALLY didn't like it, couldn't you just explain to him that you're not looking to date anybody because you have issues or whatever? Dumpin' coffee on him is basically mating dance behavior For jerks like you.

No it isn't! He just doesn't get the hint.

Seriously though, does he really bother you? 'Cause iP he's creeping you out we could always break his elbows Steven Seagal style next time he comes in.

He's not CREEPY, I just think he's an idiot who's watched too many John Cusack movies where persistence gets the girl no matter how big an ass you make of yourself.

I wish I could just get a couple days' BREAK, you know? I have enough to worry about WITHOUT random boys interrupting my life.

Hey Faye, is-

Oh For FUCK'S SAKE! NO! NOT TODAY! FUCK OFF!

HOT DRINKS

Coffee

Latte

Espresso

Cappuccino

Mocha

COLD DRINKS

Iced Coffee

Iced Latte

Iced Tea

Iced Cappucino

Iced Mocha

Whoa, what's her problem? I locked myself out of my apartment and needed to pick up the spare key I gave you.

Just bad timing on your part. Try not to get stuck in any air vents on the way home.

Huh?

The pigeons are angry and the Firefighters smell bad.

I am so confused right now.

Welcome to the MC Escher drawing that has been my morning.

"The eagle has left the nest." "Are you speaking in code?" "No, there was literally an eagle nesting on our roof."

Whoa, who's your hot friend?

This is Eve. She's also an Apple robot! Sorta.

Oh yeah? Ever thought about dual bootin' Windows, sweet-cheeks? C'mon, don't be shy! I'll show you my dll files if you show me your-

Bluhhhhhhhhhhh

BOOP

That's right, baby. I'm a smooth operator. Er, operating system. You know what I mean.

Eve is from the comic Applegeeks!

129

Whoa, jeez Dora!

COOKIE. NOW. IN YOUR MOUTH.

I have been boobed in the face by my hairdresser so many times, she's really short and I'm really tall

Dora looks really cute in pigtails. I should bring that hairstyle back for her.

Poor Tai, she really wanted to be in the band!

Maybe Bon Jovi is really good at the drums, I dunno

This is why I am not allowed to own a drumkit.

Gwar play pretty fast, I think the gong-farts happen every other measure.

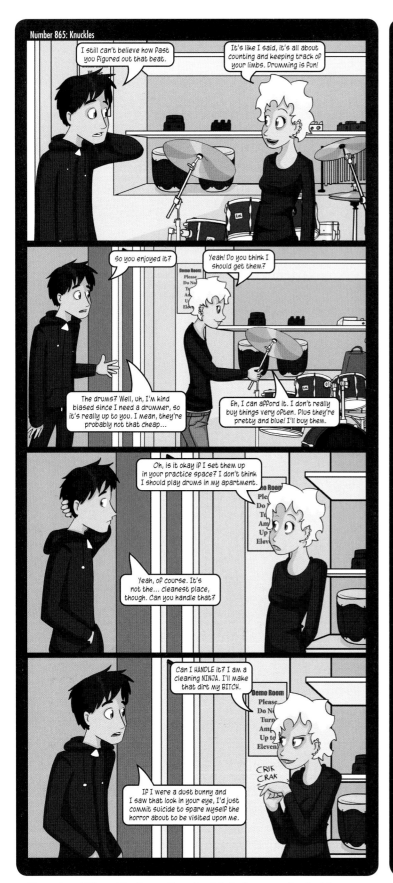

Hannelore Ellicott-Chatham: Cleaning Ninja (out now for the Xbox 360 and Playstation 3)

True love means popping hard to reach pimples on your partner's back sometimes

The destroyer is your socks!

Faye I am pretty sure Robocop was not written by Jane Austen

My seester vas once beeten by a moose

To this day, this may be the cutest comic I have ever written.

To be fair, sometimes Sven IS banging someone.

They keep a bucket of hagfish behind the bar for this very purpose.

Well, at least her finger's not broken.

Pintsize is actually in there by himself, the other two robots are hallucinations.

138

Back when I played FPSes, my handle was "an angry bear" so when I killed someone it would say "so-and-so was killed by an angry bear"

It's kind of shocking to go back and see how violent and defensive Faye used to be. She's changed a lot over the years.

Maybe a chupacabra with irritable bowel syndrome

Spoiler: Dora hasn't killed Sven yet

I made a t-shirt out of this comic, it sold pretty well

MY TWO FAVORITE COLORS

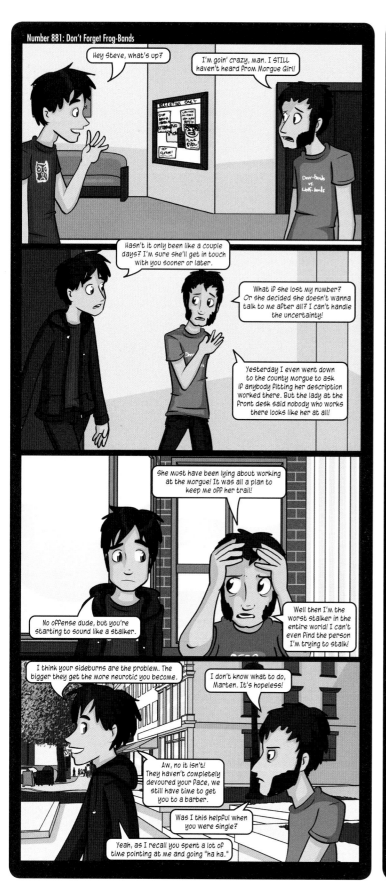

I wish I could grow sideburns like that :(

Marten is wearing a t-shirt with owls on it, years before owls became a big hipster thing. Questionable Content: trendsetter.

The sandwich place they're in was really good but it closed not too long after this comic originally ran :(

Insert Pulp Fiction reference here

Q: How many webcartoonists does it take to screw in a lightbulb? A: Who needs lightbulbs when you have the glow of your Cintiq?

Mayonnaise is just eggs from really lazy chickens! Oh god I just grossed myself out

If giraffes can sleep standing up, I don't see why people can't.

And it's a LITTLE spoon!

They offered an IV service for a while, but it was shut down by the health department.

Live eels or dead eels?

Whoa how did she do that thing with her voice in panel 4 D:

Librarians party HARD.

Rule #1 of having roommates is to invest in a good pair of headphones.

He's also her grandfather. Time travel is confusing.

Number 895: Foley

Set off some fireworks, play with a theremin, release a bunch of guinea pigs into the living room...

Number 896: Wait, On Him Or Her?

...On the boy or on Hannelore?

Cleanpocalypse Now

That shirt is preposterous, and also something that American Apparel actually sold for a while.

Aw man, this collection doesn't end with a fart joke.

Bonus Art

Here's some fun other stuff I drew around the same time as the comics in this volume. Enjoy!

I have no idea what the original context for this was. Maybe…maybe there wasn't any.

Concept sketches for that stupid vespabot thing augh so horrible.

I drew this right around the time I discovered the French death metal band Gojira. Their record "From Mars to Sirius" is one of my favorite albums of all time.

This was filler art I posted during the holidays. I made it available as a coloring-book-style page for readers to color, and they came up with some crazy versions! Now here it is in this book, for YOU to color if you want to. (Warning: this paper does not take crayons very well, so just do your best.)

Random police lady I guess?

I couldn't find the hi-rez art for Comic 791 — sometimes these things go missing. (I blame ghosts.) I re-drew the version that you see on page 98, but here's what the original looked like.

Random practice sketch of Dora. That posture is crazy!

These drawings were turned into a couple big cardboard cutouts I used for conventions.

The cake mix is a LIE!

QC ♥s Valve

JEPH JACQUES 2007

If I remember correctly, I drew this after I met Valve's Gabe Newell at a convention and fanboyed all over him.

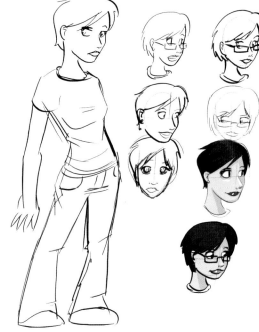

Character sketches.

More character sketches and a creepy headless torso.

A portrait I did of my friend Liz, who as far as I know is not actually a fan of Stryper but WHATEVER.

This was an intentionally ridiculous parody of hypersexualized Final Fantasy heroines. Needs more superfluous angel wings, I think.

The girl would turn out to be Penelope, and the guy would turn out to be Elliott (who doesn't show up for another 1200 strips or so!)

I have no idea what this is from but that tentacle monster is pretty cute :3

It's a bit of a QC tradition, each Thanksgiving, to see what turkeys think of what's been going on in the strip. Consider all this turkey talk 100% CANON.

This strip was written by an English-language student in Korea! It is absolutely brilliant.

ORGANIC, FREE-RANGE COMIC STRIPS
SUSTAINABLY GROWN IN BRAINS WORLDWIDE